To
Amy & David
Christmas 1977
From
David

Berran

My Bible Friends

To

Brian and Bruce
Randy and Diana

And

all the boys and girls
who like Bible stories

Library of Congress Catalog Card No. 76-55834

My Bible Friends

Etta B. Degering/Book Two

Illustrated by Robert Berran, Manning de V. Lee, William Dolwick, and William Heaslip

The stories in this book are—

Jesus and the Storm

Jesus and the Children

Samuel, the Little Priest

David, the Youngest Boy

Published and Copyrighted © 1963, 1977 by the
REVIEW AND HERALD PUBLISHING ASSOCIATION
Washington, D.C.

Jesus and the Storm

Jesus stood in a boat—
    a fishing boat with oars and a sail—
    and talked to the many people
    who had come to hear Him.
All day long Jesus told them stories.
When it was evening Jesus said to His helpers,
    "Let us cross over to the other side
    of the lake and rest."

Jesus' helpers untied the boat.
They pushed it from the shore
    and raised the sail.
One man sat in the back of the boat
    to guide it with the steering tiller.
The boat moved slowly at first, and then faster
    across the quiet blue water.

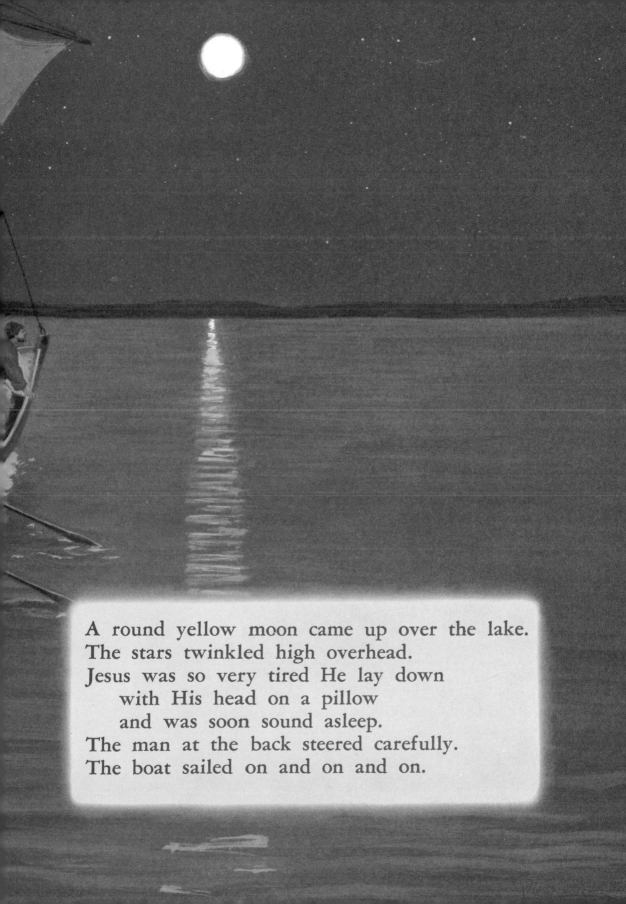

A round yellow moon came up over the lake.
The stars twinkled high overhead.
Jesus was so very tired He lay down
     with His head on a pillow
     and was soon sound asleep.
The man at the back steered carefully.
The boat sailed on and on and on.

Suddenly a fierce wind began to blow.
It blew a black cloud over the moon.
It blew black clouds over the stars.
It whipped the water into huge angry waves.
The waves tossed the boat this way,
    and that way, and up and down.
There was lightning!
There was thunder!

The man at the tiller tried to steer the boat,
but he couldn't.
Other men tried to row the boat with oars,
but they couldn't.
Water filled the boat. It began to sink.
The men were afraid. They woke Jesus—
"Lord save us; we perish!" they cried.
Jesus heard their cry for help.
He felt the angry wind.
He saw the lightning flash.
He heard the noisy thunder.

But He was not afraid.
He stood up and said to the wind and waves,
    "Peace—be still."
The wind stopped blowing. The waves were still.
The clouds went away, and the stars twinkled again.
The boat sailed on the sparkling path
    that the moon made on the water,
    and crossed to the other side of the lake.
"Why were you afraid?" Jesus asked His helpers.
"Why were you afraid when I was with you?"

Jesus says to boys and girls today—
"Don't be afraid when the lightning flashes,
    and the thunder crashes,
    and the strong winds blow."
"I am with you always," says Jesus,
    "in the dark and in the storm,
I will never leave you. Don't be afraid."

Jesus and the Children

Mark and Sara were waiting
  with Mother and baby Esther
  to see Jesus.
Other children were waiting with their mothers.
Jesus' helpers frowned at them—
  "Can't you see that Jesus is busy?
  He has no time for children."

Mark and Sara, and Mother with baby Esther
  turned slowly away.
Mark hung his head, and watched
  the dust of the path squish up
  between his brown toes.
Sara looked back at Jesus. A tear
  ran down her cheek.

Then they heard Jesus say to His helpers,
    "Suffer the little children to come unto me,
    and forbid them not."
All the children ran to Jesus.
Jesus took baby Esther on His lap.
He smiled and touched Sara's cheek
    where the tear had run down.
He put His hand on Mark's head.
The children took turns standing close to Jesus.
    He told them stories.

On the way home Mark whistled a happy tune.
Sara skipped ahead, and then she waited
    and took Mother's hand.
"I wish we could see Jesus every day," she said.
"Maybe," said Mother, "maybe soon
    Jesus will come to the Temple."

One day Mark and Sara
     heard people singing the hosanna song.
They ran to see why the people were singing.
They saw Jesus riding on a colt
     coming down the road.
People were laying their coats on the road
     for Him to ride over.
Boys were waving palm branches and shouting.
Girls were tossing flowers and singing.

"May we go with Jesus?" asked Mark.

"May we?" said Sara.

Mark's father cut a palm branch for him, and
    Mother helped Sara fill a basket with flowers.

Mark waved his palm branch and shouted,
    "Hosanna to the Son of David, Hosanna, Hosanna!"

Sara tossed flowers on the road and sang,
    "Hosanna, Hosanna!"

It was like a big parade. It made Jesus happy
    to hear the children shout and sing.

The parade came to the top of a hill.
Jesus stopped the colt,
    and looked down over the hill.
The boys stopped waving
    their palm branches and looked.
The girls stopped tossing flowers and looked.
All the people stopped
    and looked down over the hill.
What did they see down over the hill?

There was a brook down over the hill,
a sing-along, laugh-along brook,
but they were not looking at the brook.
There was a city with a high stone wall
down over the hill,
but they were not looking
at the city with the high stone wall.

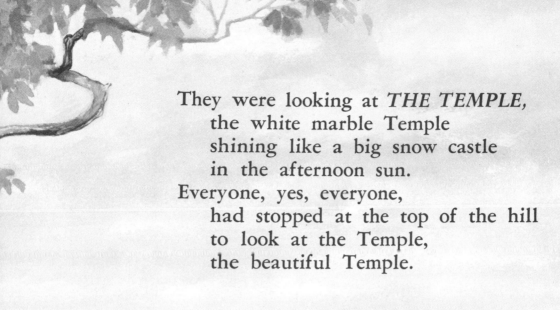

They were looking at *THE TEMPLE*,
    the white marble Temple
    shining like a big snow castle
    in the afternoon sun.
Everyone, yes, everyone,
    had stopped at the top of the hill
    to look at the Temple,
    the beautiful Temple.

The next day Mark and Sara and many other children
    went with Jesus and His friends to the Temple.
But when they got there,
    the sounds coming from the Temple
    didn't sound like a Temple at all.
There was no sound of singing and praying.
It wasn't quiet-like and hush-like,
    with people tiptoeing when they walked.
Instead—there was a terrible rackety noise!

M. de V. Lee

Traders had brought to the Temple
    cattle and sheep and doves
    to sell for offerings.
They shouted, "Buy cattle for your offering."
    "Buy sheep for your offering."
    "Buy doves for your offering."
Moneychangers were there, clinking their money.
It didn't seem like a Temple at all—not at all.
It was like a noisy market place.

M. deV. Lee

Jesus stood in the doorway—
The cattle traders looked at Him.
The sheep traders looked at Him.
The dove traders looked at Him.
They all stopped their shouting and selling.
The moneychangers stopped clinking their money.
Everyone looked at Jesus and waited
    to see what He would do.
Jesus raised His arm. He said,
    "TAKE THESE THINGS HENCE!"

Such a hurrying and a scurrying!
The traders hustled the cattle out.
They rushed the sheep out.
They grabbed the dove cages and ran.
The moneychangers didn't even stop
    to take their money.
All the grown-up people ran away from Jesus.

But the children didn't run away from Jesus.
Mark and Sara and all the children
    crowded close around Him.
Jesus told them stories.
He took the little ones on His knee.
A little boy went to sleep on His lap.

Then the sick people came to Jesus.
A boy with a hurt leg came hobbling on crutches.
Jesus put His hand on the hurt leg
    and made it well.
The boy threw away his crutches.
Now he could walk. He could run! He could jump!

A father and mother brought
    their sick little girl to Jesus.
She was so sick they carried her in a hammock.
Jesus took her small thin hand in His. He said,
    "Be well, little girl, be well."
The little girl sat up and smiled. She was well.

A boy led a blind man to Jesus.
The blind man's eyes were tight shut.
He had never seen a tree or a house—not anything.
Jesus made his eyes see.
And the first thing the blind man ever saw
    was the lovely face of Jesus.

The children were so happy
   when they saw the sick people made well,
   they again waved palm branches
   and sang the hosanna song.
The grown-up people who had run away came back.
They looked in at the Temple doors
   and heard the children singing.
They said to Jesus, "Make the children be still."
But Jesus liked to hear the children sing.
He didn't want them to be still.

It was time to close the Temple doors.
Tomorrow the children would come back
   to hear more stories.
Jesus wanted them to come. He had said,
   "Suffer the little children to come unto me,
   and forbid them not."

Mark and Sara waved good-by to Jesus.
All the way home they sang the hosanna song,
"Hosanna to the Son of David,
Hosanna, Hosanna!"

Samuel, the Little Priest

Once there was a little boy named Samuel
    who was brought to the Temple
    to live with Priest Eli.
Priest Eli took Samuel's hand and walked
    with him in the Temple court.
Samuel saw the evening fire burning on the altar.
He saw the shiny washbasin and the cloth fence.
He heard priests blowing trumpets and people praying.
The tiny bells on Priest Eli's robe *tinkle-tinkle-*
    tinkled, as Samuel and he walked together.

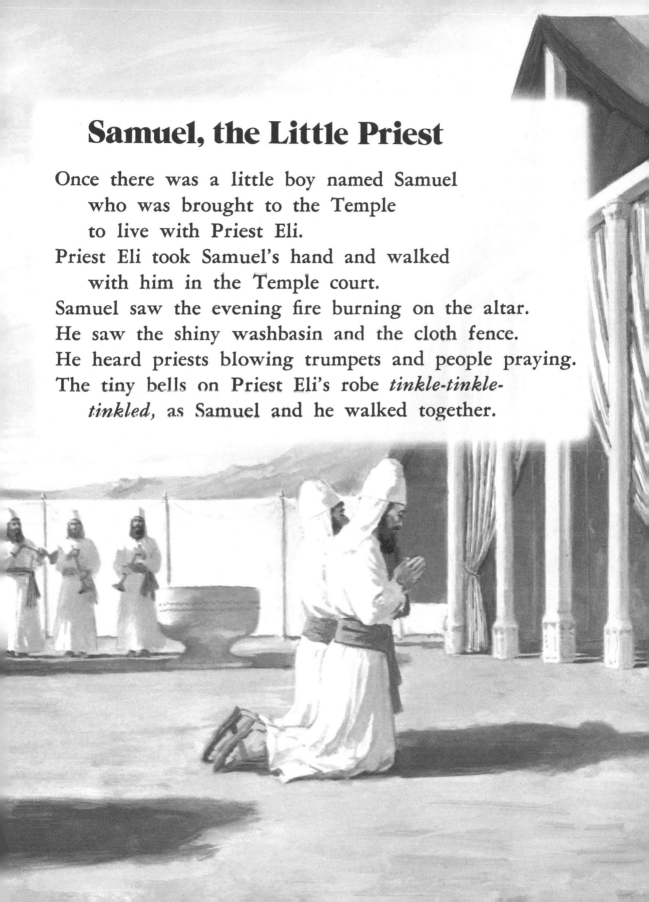

Priest Eli and Samuel stopped at the Temple door.
Everything in the Temple was made of gold—
There was a golden table, a golden altar, and
    a golden candlestick with seven golden lamps.
Samuel watched as Priest Eli went inside the Temple
    to burn sweet-smelling incense
    on the golden altar, and pray to God.
Samuel hoped that someday God would choose him
    to be a priest—a priest like Eli.
Then *he* would do God's special work in the Temple.

Samuel helped Priest Eli with the Temple work.
Every morning he got up early
    to open the curtain doors of the Temple.
The curtains were purple and red and blue.
Samuel was a busy worker—
    He brought wood for the fire.
    He carried water for the shiny washbasin.
    He dusted the golden furniture.

Samuel helped Priest Eli
    fill the seven golden lamps with oil.
The lamps must be kept burning,
    all through the day,
    all through the night.
The oil made the lamps burn with a yellow light.
When it began to grow dark
    Samuel closed the Temple doors.
And then came the time he liked best.
    It was the story time.

Samuel brought his favorite book,
    and sat on a stool beside Priest Eli.
Samuel's book did not have pages to turn.
It was a long, long piece of paper
    rolled into a roll, called a scroll.
Priest Eli unrolled the book and read him stories
    about Joseph, and Moses, and God.
Much too soon the stories were over,
    and it was time to go to bed.

Samuel said good night to Priest Eli.
He spread his bed out on the floor.
Then he said his prayer and lay down to sleep.
Priest Eli slept in a room nearby.
If he needed anything in the night
     he would call Samuel.

Samuel went to sleep.
He was *sound* asleep one night
    when a voice called, "S-a-m-u-e-l!"
Samuel jumped up. He ran to Priest Eli.
    "Here I am, for you called me."
But Priest Eli said,
    "I did not call, lie down again."
Samuel went back and lay down.

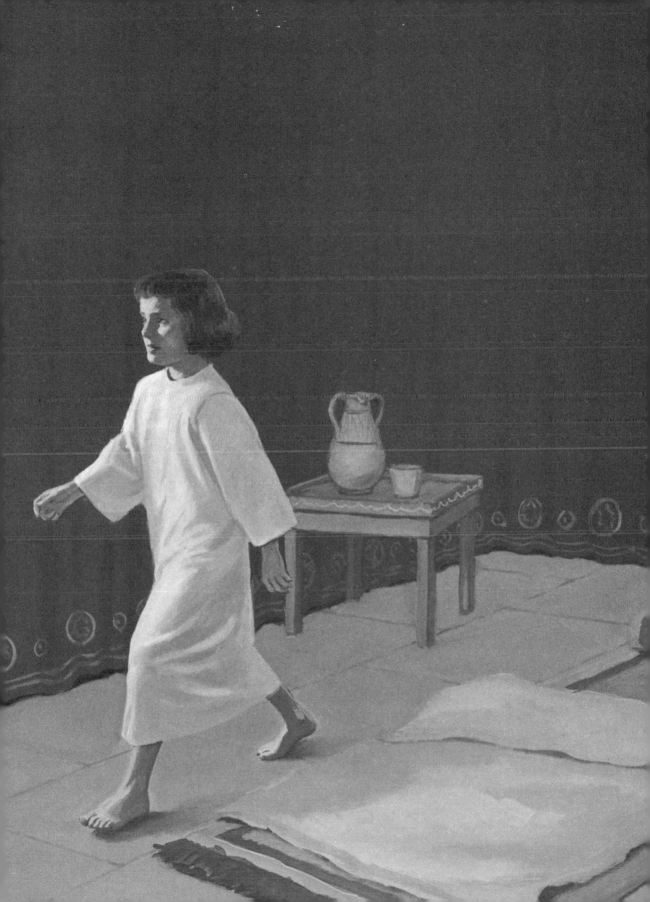

Before Samuel could go to sleep,
   the voice called again, "S-a-m-u-e-l!"
Samuel jumped up quickly and ran to Priest Eli.
   "Here I am, for you called me."
But Priest Eli said,
   "I did not call, my son, lie down again."
Samuel went slowly back to bed.
He was sure someone had called him.

Almost before Samuel's head was on his pillow,
   the voice called, "S-a-m-u-e-l!"
Samuel jumped up and ran to Priest Eli.
   "Here I am, for you *did* call me."
Then Priest Eli knew that it must be God
   who was calling Samuel.
He said, "Go lie down and if He calls again, say,
   'Speak, Lord, for thy servant heareth.' "
Once more Samuel lay down on his bed.

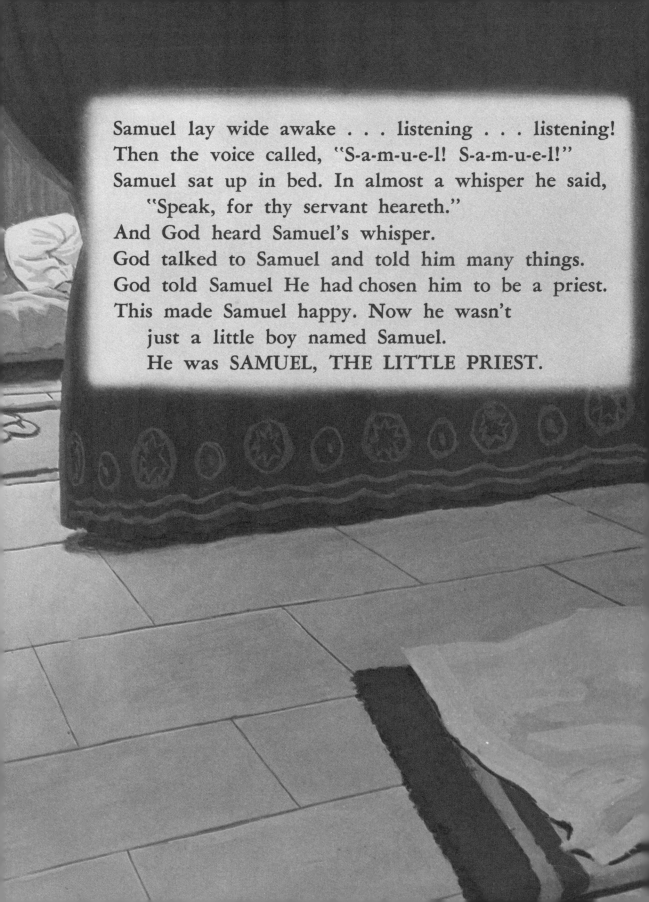

Samuel lay wide awake . . . listening . . . listening!
Then the voice called, "S-a-m-u-e-l! S-a-m-u-e-l!"
Samuel sat up in bed. In almost a whisper he said,
   "Speak, for thy servant heareth."
And God heard Samuel's whisper.
God talked to Samuel and told him many things.
God told Samuel He had chosen him to be a priest.
This made Samuel happy. Now he wasn't
   just a little boy named Samuel.
He was SAMUEL, THE LITTLE PRIEST.

David, the Youngest Boy

Eight brothers standing in a row!
The youngest boy at the end of the row is David.
David and his brothers lived on a farm
    near a small town.
David was a shepherd boy.
He took care of his father's sheep.

To David's town came Samuel the prophet.
The prophet invited all the people
    to a special feast.
David's brothers were going to the feast.
David's father was going to the feast.
But the brothers said to David,
    "You are too young to go.
    You stay home with the sheep."

David took his harp under his arm.
He tucked his sling in his belt.
He opened the gate to the sheeppen.
    "Come, sheep! Come, lambs!" he called.
The sheep followed David down the path.
Black Lamb and Curly Lamb walked
    one on each side of David.

David led the sheep to a green grassy place.
While the older sheep nibbled grass
    Black Lamb and Curly Lamb
    played jumping games and bunting games
    with the other lambs.
David played tunes on his harp
    and kept close watch of the sheep.

Black Lamb began to wander away up over the hill.
David put down his harp and ran after him.
He brought Black Lamb back to the flock.
Then David saw a weed that would
    make the sheep sick if they ate it.
He pulled up the weed and threw it away.
A jackal sneaked around a rock toward the sheep.
David stamped his foot, and the jackal *ran*.

David took his sling from his belt.
It was a long, long sling
    that his father had made for him
    from strong brown leather.
He put a smooth stone in the sling.
Now what should he hit? That red rock?
    He would try.
Around and around and around he swung his sling.
Zing-g-g-g went the stone!
Ping! It hit the red rock.

David put another stone in his sling.
He would aim for that round black hole
in the tree.
Around and around and around he swung the sling.
Zing-g-g-g went the stone
straight into the round black hole
in the tree.

Then David heard a noise.
It wasn't a *hopping, thumping* noise
   like a rabbit running through the grass.
No . . . it wasn't a rabbit.

It wasn't a *picking, pecking* noise
   like a bird pecking on a tree.
No . . . it wasn't a bird.

It was a *sn-uffing, gr-r-uffing* noise
   like a big animal prowling around.
It was——

A BEAR! A fierce brown bear! And he was
    sneaking closer, and closer, and closer,
    to where the lambs were playing.
The bear crept up behind a bush
    ready to snatch Curly Lamb
    as she ran by.

Quickly David put a stone in his sling.
He ran straight toward the bear.
Around and around and around he swung the sling.
Zing-g-g-g went the stone!
It hit the fierce brown bear. The bear fell dead.

David picked up frightened little Curly Lamb
    and carried her in his arms.
Black Lamb kept close by his side.
"Come sheep! Come lambs!" called David,
    and he led them to a place
    where they would be safe.
While the older sheep nibbled the new green grass,
    Black Lamb and Curly Lamb again
    played jumping games with the other lambs,
    and David played tunes on his harp.

Now while David was watching the sheep,
   Samuel the prophet made ready the feast.
David's father was at the feast.
David's brothers were at the feast.
Before they sat down to eat,
   the prophet said to David's father,
   "Have your boys walk before me, one by one.
   Today God will choose one of them
   for something very special."

David's oldest brother walked before the prophet.
"No, it is not this boy," said the prophet.
The next oldest brother walked before the prophet.
"No, it is not this boy," said the prophet.
And then the next oldest brother
    walked before the prophet.
The prophet shook his head.

"No, it is not this boy."

One by one——
    David's brothers walked before the prophet,
    but each time the prophet said,
    "No, it is not this boy."
Then the prophet asked David's father,
    "Have you no other boys?"
"Only the youngest boy. He is herding the sheep."
"Send and get him," said the prophet.

David came running,
    his harp under his arm, his sling in his belt.
His cheeks were red. The wind blew his hair.
"Walk before the prophet, David,"
    said his father.
David walked before the prophet.
"This is the one," said the prophet.
"This is the boy God chooses."
The prophet poured sweet-smelling oil
    on David's head
    to show that he was the chosen one.

"Now we shall sit down to the feast,"
   said the prophet.
A place was made for David, and he sat
   with his father and brothers.
Why had David been chosen? What would he do?
No one knew. It was a secret.
David's father didn't know.
David's brothers didn't know. David didn't know.
Only the prophet and God knew
   that someday——

David would be *KING*.
And David would be as good a king
as he was a shepherd boy.